USE YOUR HEAD

TONY HUSBAND

SPHERE BOOKS LIMITED
London & Sydney

First published in Great Britain by Sphere Books Ltd 1984
30–32 Gray's Inn Road, London WC1X 8JL
Reprinted 1984 (twice)
Copyright © 1984 by Tony Husband

'To Carole, with love and thanks'

TRADE
MARK

Reproduced, printed and bound in Great Britain by
Hazell Watson & Viney Limited,
Aylesbury, Bucks